RYA motor cruising syllabus & logbook

Revised and updated 2003
by Jonathan Mendez

Published by
The Royal Yachting Association
RYA House Ensign Way Hamble
Southampton SO31 4YA
Tel: 0845 345 0400
Fax: 0845 345 0329
Email: info@rya.org.uk
Web: www.rya.org.uk

Contents

	page
RYA Motor Cruising Scheme Structure	inside front cover
Introduction to RYA Cruising Scheme	3
RYA Training Centres - Inspection and safety - Support literature	
RYA/MCA Certificates of Competence	4
An explanation of the Coastal Skipper, Yachtmaster Offshore and Yachtmaster Ocean Schemes, exam structure and syllabi	
RYA Shorebased Courses	11
Navigation and seamanship theory courses	
Day Skipper	13
Coastal Skipper/Yachtmaster Offshore	16
Yachtmaster Ocean	20
Diesel Engine Course	22
A beginner's course in preventative maintenance and minor repairs for marine diesels	
RYA/MCA Basic Sea Survival Course	23
Essential theory about survival techniques and practical experience in the water with liferafts	
Radar Course	24
An introduction to the basic principles of marine radar as a safety and navigation aid	
Practical Courses	25
An explanation and the syllabus for:-	
Helmsman	28
Day Skipper Tidal	31
Day Skipper Non-Tidal	34
Coastal Skipper Tidal	37
Coastal Skipper Non-Tidal	39
Personal Log	41
Attach your Certificates Here	51

| *Indicates a change to the previous edition*

This book is effective for examinations, shorebased courses and practical courses from 1 January 2003

2

GW00669741

How to find the right course

Before taking a course you should look carefully experience requirement and, if necessary, discuss you of ability with a training centre. The intention of the courses is to improve your ability in the sport and therefore allow you to gain more enjoyment from motor cruising. Attempting a course above your current level of ability is counterproductive and will be less use than one which is realistically pitched at your level.

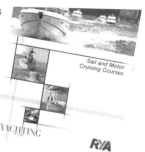

To select a Training Centre that will meet your needs, visit the RYA website for a list of centres www.rya.org.uk or call the RYA 0845 345 0400 for a free courses' brochure.

What is an RYA Training Centre?

Safety is a priority for the RYA. Each RYA Training Centre is regularly inspected for standards of tuition, facilities and equipment, as laid down by the RYA Training Division and published in the guidance notes.

All RYA Training Centres must have qualified staff, suitable boats and adequate safety cover and should display a Certificate of Recognition specifying the activities for which they are recognised. They are also required to carry public liability insurance.

At the end of your course, the Principal or Chief Instructor will decide whether certificates are to be awarded. If the Principal decides that further practice is necessary before awarding you a certificate, the reasons will be explained to you.

Learning Resources

The RYA produces a wide range of materials to help you learn, from course handbooks to training videos. These can be obtained through RYA schools and the RYA website or simply phone the RYA and ask for this free catalogue.

The RYA is committed to encouraging both women and men to participate in sailing. For clarity only, the text of this logbook is written in the masculine gender eg Man overboard.

Certificates of Competence

Examinations

RYA/MCA Coastal Skipper, Yachtmaster Offshore and Yachtmaster Ocean Certificates of Competence are gained by examination, conducted by RYA Yachtmaster Examiners who are independent of training centres. The previous experience required before taking these examinations, and the scope of the syllabus, is shown on the following pages. There is no requirement to attend a course before taking an examination, unless the exam is taken outside the UK, although many candidates have found it helpful to brush up their skills at a school.

Coastal Skipper and Yachtmaster Offshore Certificates of Competence can be used as evidence of competence to command a wide variety of vessels. Skippers should ensure that they are familiar with the handling and other characteristics of any vessel they take to sea.

Own boat exams
For the practical examination for Coastal Skipper and Yachtmaster Offshore candidates must provide a motor cruiser not less than 7 metres LOA, in sound, seaworthy condition and equipped to the standard set out in the *RYA Boat Safety Handbook* (C8). The motor cruiser must be equipped with a full and up-to-date set of charts and navigational publications and be efficiently crewed, as the examiner will not take part in the management of the motor cruiser during the examination.

Booking an examination
To book an exam in the UK
- contact an exam centre listed on page 57 or
- book directly with the RYA at www.rya.org.uk

Exams through a training centre
If you take a course at an RYA Training Centre the exam can be arranged through the centre.

Overseas exams
Overseas examinations must be organised through an RYA Training Centre recognised for practical cruising courses. The school must notify the RYA of any overseas examinations, and the location must be approved by the RYA.

Validity of Certificates
No Certificate of Competence is required on board British flag pleasure vessels of less than 24 metres load line length.

Megayacht qualifications
Commercial pleasure vessels of more than 24 metres loadline length are subject to the Training and Certification Guidance Part 21 of MGN 195(M). Full details are given on the website www.megayachtcode.com. RYA Certificates of Competence with a commercial endorsement can be used as an entry into these qualifications.

Vessels under 24m in length used for sport or recreation on a commercial basis.
Vessels used for sport or recreation on a commercial basis are subject to Merchant Shipping legislation. The use of Coastal Skipper, Yachtmaster Offshore and Yachtmaster Ocean certificates is permitted for the skippers of these vessels, provided that the certificates are endorsed 'Valid for pleasure vessels up to 24m in length used for commercial purposes'.

To obtain this endorsement an applicant must obtain a Medical Fitness Certificate and attend a Basic Sea Survival Course.

Medical fitness forms and details of Basic Sea Survival Courses are available from the RYA.

The endorsement for commercial use is valid for five years. It may be renewed by providing evidence of continuing satisfactory service at sea as skipper or mate of a small commercial vessel and a Medical Fitness Certificate.

Withdrawal of Certificates

The Yachtmaster Qualification Panel reserves the right to withdraw certificates at any time if due cause is shown.

Previous experience requirement

Grade of examination	Minimum seatime[1]	Form of examination	Certificate required before examination
RYA/MCA Coastal Skipper	30 days 2 days as skipper 800 miles 12 night hours [2]	Practical	Restricted (VHF only) Radio Operator's Certificate First Aid Certificate
RYA/MCA Yachtmaster Offshore	50 days 5 days as skipper 2500 miles 5 passages over 60M, including 2 overnight and 2 as skipper	Practical	Restricted (VHF only) Radio Operator's Certificate First Aid Certificate
RYA/MCA Yachtmaster Ocean	Ocean passage as skipper or mate of watch	Oral and assessment of sights taken at sea[3]	RYA/MCA Yachtmaster Offshore Certificate and Yachtmaster Ocean Shorebased Course Completion Certificate

1 Within 10 years of examination
2 If you have a Coastal Skipper Practical Course Completion Certificate the seatime requirement is reduced to 20 days (2 days as skipper), 400 miles and 12 night hours
3 Written exam in lieu of shorebased course completion certificate

Coastal Skipper Certificate of Competence

The Coastal Skipper has the knowledge needed to skipper a motor cruiser on coastal cruises but does not necessarily have the experience needed to undertake longer passages.

Pre-exam requirement

To take the practical examination, candidates must be aged 17 or over and require:

Radio Operator's Qualification - A Restricted (VHF only) Radio Operator's Certificate or a GMDSS Short Range Certificate or higher grade of marine radio certificate.

First Aid - A valid First Aid Certificate. First Aid qualifications held by Police, Fire and Armed Services are also acceptable.

Seatime - 800 miles logged within 10 years prior to examination, 30 days living on board, 2 days as skipper and 12 night hours.

For holders of the Coastal Skipper Practical Course Completion Certificate, the seatime requirement is reduced to: 400 miles, 20 days living on board, 12 night hours, 2 days as skipper.

Exam duration

The exam will take about 6 to 10 hours for one candidate and 8 to 14 hours for two. Candidates will be set tasks to demonstrate their ability as a Coastal Skipper and may also be asked questions on any part of the syllabus for all practical and shorebased courses up to Coastal Skipper.

Yachtmaster Offshore Certificate of Competence

The Yachtmaster Offshore is competent to skipper a motor cruiser on any passage during which the vessel is no more than 150 miles from harbour.

Pre-exam requirement

To take the practical examination, candidates must be aged 18 or over and require:

Radio Operator's Qualification - A restricted (VHF only) Radio Operator's Certificate or a GMDSS Short Range Certificate or higher grade of marine radio certificate.

First Aid - A valid First Aid Certificate. First Aid qualifications held by Police, Fire and Armed Services are also acceptable.

Seatime - 50 days, 2,500 miles, including at least five passages over 60 miles measured along the rhumb line from the port of departure to the destination, acting as skipper for at least two of these passages and including two which have involved overnight passages. Five days experience as skipper.

Exam duration

The yachtmaster exam will take about 8 to 12 hours for one candidate and 10 to 18 hours for two. Candidates will be set tasks to demonstrate their ability as skipper of an offshore motor cruiser and may also be asked questions on any part of the syllabus for all courses except Yachtmaster Ocean.

Conversion Practical Examinations

Holders of the Yachtmaster Offshore Sail Certificate may take a conversion examination to obtain the Yachtmaster Offshore Power Certificate. Yachtmaster Offshore Power candidates may convert to sail. The same rules apply but the exam may be slightly longer.

The exam fee set by the RYA is approximately half that of a full examination.

Pre-exam requirement
At least half the required experience for Yachtmaster must be in a power vessel such as a motor cruiser i.e: 1250 miles • 25 days • 3 days as skipper • 3 passages over 60 miles including 1 overnight and 1 as skipper.

Exam duration
The exam will take about three hours. The examiner may ask questions or set tasks on any part of the syllabus but will concentrate on those sections which are markedly different in a motor cruiser e.g. boat handling, passage planning, radar.

Coastal Skipper and Yachtmaster Offshore Syllabi

Candidates may be given the opportunity to demonstrate knowledge or competence in the areas listed below. In each section the examiner will expect to see the candidate take full responsibility for the management of the vessel and crew.

In Yachtmaster Offshore exams the candidate will be expected to demonstrate competence based on broad experience.

In Coastal Skipper exams the candidate will be expected to demonstrate understanding but may not have had the opportunity to practise all aspects of the syllabus under a range of different weather conditions.

1. International Regulations for Preventing Collisions at Sea
Questions will be confined to the International Regulations and although candidates must be aware of the existence of Local Regulations, they will not be expected to memorise specific local regulations.

- General rules (1-3)
- Steering and sailing rules (4-19)
- Lights and shapes (20-31)
- Sound and light signals (32-37)
- Signals for vessels fishing in close proximity (Annex II)
- Distress signals (Annex IV)

2. Safety

Candidates will be expected to know what safety equipment should be carried on board a vessel, based either on the recommendations in the *RYA Boat Safety Handbook (C8)*, the Special Regulations of the ORC or the Codes of Practice for the Safety of Small Commercial Vessels. In particular, candidates must know the responsibilities of a skipper in relation to:

- Safety harnesses
- Lifejackets
- Distress flares
- Fire prevention and fighting
- Liferafts
- Knowledge of rescue procedures. Helicopter rescue

3. Boat handling

Candidates for Coastal Skipper examinations will be expected to answer questions or demonstrate ability in simple situations only. Candidates for Yachtmaster Offshore will be expected to answer questions or demonstrate ability in more complex situations and will also be expected to show a higher level of expertise:

- Coming to and weighing anchor in various conditions of wind and tide
- All berthing and unberthing situations in various conditions of wind and tide ·
- Recovery of man overboard
- Towing under open sea conditions and in confined areas
- Boat handling in confined areas
- Boat handling in heavy weather
- Helmsmanship
- Use of warps for securing in an alongside berth and for shifting berth or winding

4. General seamanship, including maintenance

- Properties, use and care of synthetic fibre ropes
- Knots
- General deck-work at sea and in harbour
- Engine operations and routine checks

5. Responsibilities of skipper

- Can skipper a motor cruiser and manage the crew
- Communication with crew
- Delegation of responsibility and watch-keeping organisation
- Preparing vessel for sea and for adverse weather
- Tactics for heavy weather and restricted visibility
- Emergency and distress situations
- Victualling for a cruise and feeding at sea
- Customs procedures
- Standards of behaviour and courtesy

6. Navigation

- Charts, navigational publications and sources of navigational information
- Chartwork including position fixing and shaping course to allow for tidal stream and leeway
- Tide and tidal stream calculations
- Buoyage and visual aids to navigation
- Instruments including compasses, logs, echo sounders, radio navaids and chartwork instruments
- Passage planning and navigational tactics
- Pilotage techniques
- Navigational records
- Limits of navigational accuracy and margins of safety
- Lee shore dangers
- Use of electronic navigation aids for passage planning and passage navigation
- Use of waypoints and electronic routeing

7. Meteorology

- Definition of terms
- Sources of weather forecasts
- Weather systems and local weather effects
- Interpretation of weather forecasts, barometric trends and visible phenomena
- Ability to make passage planning decisions based on forecast information

8. Signals

- Candidates for Yachtmaster Offshore and Coastal Skipper must hold the Restricted (VHF only) Certificate of Competence in radiotelephony or a higher grade of certificate in radiotelephony.

Yachtmaster Ocean Certificate of Competence

The Yachtmaster Ocean is experienced and competent to skipper a yacht on passages of any length in all parts of the world.

Pre-exam requirement

All candidates must:

(i) Hold an RYA/MCA Yachtmaster Offshore Certificate of Competence. An RYA/MCA Coastal Skipper Certificate does not qualify.

(ii) Have completed, as skipper or mate of a vessel, a qualifying passage which meets the following criteria:

a) The candidate was fully involved in the planning of the passage, including selection of the route, the navigational plan, checking the material condition of the vessel and her equipment, storing with spare gear, water and victuals and organising the watch-keeping routine.

b) During the passage, a minimum non-stop distance of 600 miles must have been run by the log, the vessel must have been at sea continuously for at least 96 hours and the vessel must have been more than 50 miles from land while sailing a distance of at least 200 miles.

(iii) Hold a First Aid qualification, as for Yachtmaster Offshore.

Form of examination

The exam consists of an oral and a written test.

Oral

The candidate must provide the examiner with:

a) A narrative account of the planning and execution of the qualifying passage.

b) Navigational records, completed on board a vessel on passage, out of sight of land, showing that the candidate has navigated the vessel without the use of electronic navigational aids. The records must include as a minimum: planning, reduction and plotting of a sun-run-meridian altitude sight and a compass check carried out using the bearing of the sun, moon, a star or a planet.

During the oral test the candidate may be required to answer questions on all aspects of ocean passage making including passage planning, navigation, worldwide meteorology, crew management and vessel preparation, maintenance and repairs.

Written

The written exam will include questions on sights and sight reduction and worldwide meteorology.

Candidates who hold the Certificate of Satisfactory Completion of the RYA/MCA Yachtmaster Ocean Shorebased Course, a Royal Navy Ocean Navigation Certificate or an MCA Certificate of Competence as a Deck Officer will be exempt from the written examination.

Course Completion Certificates

The authority to award certificates of satisfactory completion of shorebased courses is delegated to RYA Training Centres, which may be Local Education Authority evening classes, clubs, sailing schools or correspondence colleges.

All instructors must hold an RYA/MCA Yachtmaster Offshore Certificate of Competence and be an active cruising skipper. All potential shorebased instructors will be asked to attend an RYA Shorebased Instructors, training and familiarisation weekend.

The school must provide a suitable classroom where all the students can undertake chartwork simultaneously.

Certificates of satisfactory completion of courses are, as the name implies, awarded only following completion of a course. The theory or written exams may not be taken as a separate entity. However, anyone who has the necessary qualifying experience may take the full practical examination for Coastal Skipper or Yachtmaster Offshore (see page 5).

Assessment during shorebased courses

A standard set of assessment papers for each course is provided. While many of these papers are used informally, some are worked under invigilation to provide an objective test of ability at the end of the course.

Layout of syllabi

An indication of the minimum recommended teaching time for each subject is given in each syllabus. The total time for each syllabus is approximately 40 hours.

The courses also include assessment papers which involve an additional 14 hours work. Sufficient time should be allowed for completion of these exercises and subsequent discussion of them, together with additional exercises set by instructors and revision which may add anything up to 100% to the minimum recommended teaching times. An indication of the depth of knowledge required is also given, the following abbreviations being used:

A Full knowledge   B Working knowledge   C Outline knowledge

International Regulations for Preventing Collisions at Sea

Students are required to have a full knowledge of the regulations before completion of the shorebased course for Coastal Skipper and Yachtmaster Offshore. There is, however, insufficient time available in the course to teach the subject fully. The RYA book *International Regulations for Preventing Collisions at Sea* (G2) or *A Seaman's Guide to the Rule of the Road* are useful books for study of the regulations.

Feedback

The student's assessment pack includes two forms requesting feedback about the courses. Please help the RYA to improve the courses by returning one to the school and the other to the RYA.

Day Skipper Shorebased Course Syllabus

A comprehensive introduction to chart work, navigation, meteorology and the basics of seamanship for Helmsmen. You will find this course invaluable if you want to learn how to start making decisions on board.

	Minimum time (hours)	Depth of knowledge
1. Nautical terms	2	
• Parts of a boat and hull		B
• General nautical terminology		B
2. Ropework	1	
• Knowledge of the properties of synthetic ropes in common use		B
3. Anchorwork	1	
• Characteristics of different types of anchor		B
• Considerations to be taken into account when anchoring		B
4. Safety	3	
• Knowledge of the safety equipment to be carried, it's stowage and use (see *RYA Boat Safety Handbook, C8*)		B
• Fire precautions and fire fighting		B
• Use of personal safety equipment, harnesses and lifejackets		B
• Ability to send a distress signal by VHF radiotelephone		B
• Basic knowledge of rescue procedures including helicopter rescue		B
5. International regulations for preventing collisions at sea	3	
• Steering and sailing rules (5, 7, 8, 9, 10 and 12-19)		A
• General rules (all other rules)		B
6. Definition of position, course and speed	1	
• Latitude and longitude		B
• Knowledge of standard navigational terms		B
• True bearings and courses		B
• The knot		C
7. Navigational charts and publications	2	
• Information shown on charts, chart symbols and representation of direction and distance		B
• Navigational publications in common use		C
• Chart correction		C

	Minimum time (hours)	Depth of knowledge
8. Navigational drawing instruments	1	
• Use of parallel rulers, dividers and proprietary plotting instruments		B
9. Compass	2	
• Application of variation		B
• Awareness of deviation and its causes		C
• Use of hand-bearing compass		B
10.Chartwork	6	
• Dead reckoning and estimated position including an awareness of leeway		B C
• Techniques of visual fixing		B
• Satellite-derived positions		B
• Use of waypoints to fix position		A
• Course to steer		B
11.Tides and tidal streams	4	
• Tidal definitions, levels and datum		B
• Tide tables		B
• Use of Admiralty method of determining tidal height at standard port and awareness of corrections for secondary ports		B
• Use of tidal diamonds and tidal stream atlases for chartwork		B
12.Visual aids to navigation	1	
• Lighthouses and beacons, light characteristics		B
13.Meteorology	3	
• Sources of broadcast meteorological information		B
• Knowledge of terms used in shipping forecasts, including the Beaufort scale, and their significance to small craft		B
• Basic knowledge of highs, lows and fronts		C

	Minimum time (hours)	Depth of knowledge
14.Passage planning	4	
• Preparation of navigational plan for short coastal passages		C
• Meteorological considerations in planning short coastal passages		C
• Use of waypoints on passage		B
• Importance of confirmation of position by an independent source		A
• Keeping a navigational record		A
15.Navigation in restricted visibility	1	
• Precautions to be taken in, and limitations imposed by, fog		B
16.Pilotage	4	
• Use of transits, leading lines and clearing lines		B
• IALA system of buoyage for Region A		B
• Use of sailing directions		B
• Pilotage plans and harbour entry		B
17.Marine environment	1	
• Responsibility for avoiding pollution and protecting the marine environment		B

Coastal Skipper/Yachtmaster Offshore Shorebased Course Syllabus

This is an advanced course in navigation and meteorology for candidates for the Coastal Skipper and Yachtmaster Offshore Certificate. The syllabus makes some provision for the revision of subjects in the Day Skipper Course but those who have not acquired the knowledge set out in the Day Skipper Course are unlikely to be able to assimilate all the subjects covered in this advanced course in the time available.

The assumed level of knowledge before starting this course is the Day Skipper Shorebased Course.

	Minimum time (hours)	Depth of knowledge
1. Position	6	
• Dead reckoning and estimated position		B
• Satellite-derived position		A
• Use of waypoints to fix position		A
• Radar fixes		B
• Techniques of visual fixing		B
• Fixes using a mixture of position lines		B
• Relative accuracy of different methods of position fixing		A
• Areas of uncertainty		C
2. The magnetic compass	2	
• Allowance for variation		B
• Change of variation with time and position		B
• Causes of deviation		B
• Swing for deviation (but not correction)		C
• Allowance for deviation		C
• Different types of compass		C
3. Tides	4	
• Causes of tides - Springs and Neaps		C
• Tide tables - sources		B
• Tidal levels and datum		B
• Standard and secondary ports		B
• Tidal anomalies (Solent, etc.)		C

	Minimum time (hours)	Depth of knowledge
4. Tidal streams	3	
• Sources of tidal information		B
• Tidal stream information in sailing directions and Yachtsmen's Almanacs		B
• Allowance for tidal streams in computing a course to steer		A
• Tide rips, overfalls and races		B
• Tidal observation buoys, beacons etc.		B
5. Buoyage	1	
• IALA system buoyage in Region A		B
• Limitations of buoys as navigational aids		C
6. Lights	1	
• Characteristics		B
• Ranges – visual, luminous and nominal		C
• Rising and dipping distances		C
• Light lists		C
7. Pilotage	3	
• Harbour regulations and control signals		A
• Methods of pre-planning		B
• Clearing lines		A
• Use of soundings		B
• Transits and leading lines		B
8. GPS and chart plotters	3	
• Principles of operation and limitations of use		A
• Raster and vector charts		C
• Datum		B
• Importance of confirmation of position by an independent source and keeping a separate record of position		A
• Importance of paper charts		B
9. Echo sounders	1/2	
• Principles of operation and limitations of use		C
10. Logs (speed and distance measuring)	1/2	
• Principles of operation and limitations of use		C

	Minimum time (hours)	Depth of knowledge
11. Deck log	$1/2$	
• Importance of log as vessel's official document		B
• Layout of log, hourly and occasional entries		B
12. Meteorology	6	
• Basic terms, the Beaufort scale		B
• Air masses		B
• Cloud types		B
• Weather patterns associated with pressure and frontal systems		B
• Sources of weather forecasts		B
• Ability to interpret a shipping forecast, weatherfax and weather satellite information		B
• Land and sea breezes		B
• Sea fog		C
• Use of a barometer as a forecasting aid		B
13. Rule of the Road	1	
• A sound knowledge of the International Regulations for Preventing Collisions at Sea, except Annexes 1 and 3		A
14. Safety at Sea	2	
• Personal safety, use of lifejackets, safety harnesses and lifelines		B
• Fire prevention and fire fighting		B
• Distress signals		B
• Coastguard and Boat Safety Scheme		C
• Preparation for heavy weather		B
• Liferafts and helicopter rescue		B
• Understanding of capabilities of vessel and basic knowledge of stability		C
15. Navigation in restricted visibility	1	
• Precautions to be taken in fog		B
• Limitations to safe navigation imposed by fog		B
• Navigation strategy in poor visibility		B

	Minimum time (hours)	Depth of knowledge
16.Passage planning	5	
• Preparation of charts and notebook for route planning and making, and use at sea		B
• Customs regulations as they apply to vessels		C
• Routine for navigating in coastal waters		B
• Strategy for course laying		B
• Use of waypoints and routes		A
• Use of weather forecast information for passage planning strategy		B
• Sources of local and national regulations		B
17.Marine environment	$^1/_2$	
• Responsibility to minimise pollution and protect the marine environment		B

Yachtmaster Ocean Shorebased Course Syllabus

This is a course in astro-navigation and worldwide meteorology which also reveals the mysteries of the sextant. It assumes a knowledge of all subjects covered in the other shorebased courses.

Minimum time (hours)

1. The earth and the celestial sphere
2

- Definition of observer's zenith and position of a heavenly body in terms of latitude, longitude, GHA and declination

- Right angle relationships, latitude and co-lat, declination and polar distance

- Relationship between GHA, longitude and LHA

- Tabulation of declination in nautical almanac

- Rate of increase of hour angle with time

2. The PZX triangle
3

- The tabulated components of the triangle, LHA, co-lat and polar distance

- The calculable components, zenith distance and azimuth

- Relationship between zenith distance and altitude

- Introduction to the tabular method of solution in the Air Navigation Tables and the basic sight form

- The use of calculators for the solution of the PZX triangle

3. The sextant
2

- Practical guide to the use and care of a sextant at sea

- Conversion of sextant altitude to true altitude

- Application of dip, index error and refraction

- Correction of side error, perpendicularity, index error and collimation error

4. Measurement of time
2

- Definition of, and relationship between, UT, LMT, standard time and zone time

- Rating of chronometers and watches

5. Meridian altitudes
2

- Forecasting time of meridian altitude

- Reduction of meridian altitude sights

6. Sun, star and other sights   5
- Reduction and plotting of sun sights using Air
- Navigation Tables

- Awareness of use of calculator for sight reduction

- The plotting of a sun-run-sun meridian altitude

- Awareness of the reduction and plotting of sights
  obtained from stars, moon and planets

7. Compass checking   1
- Use of amplitude and azimuth tables
  systems and/or calculator

8. Satellite Navigation Systems   2
- Principles and limitations of use of all systems

9. Great circle sailing   1
- Comparison of rhumb lines and great circles

- Vertices and composite tracks

- The computation of a series of rhumb lines
  approximating to a great circle by use of gnomonic
  and Mercator projections

10. Meteorology   8
- General pressure distribution and prevailing
  winds over the oceans of the world

- Tropical revolving storms, seasonal occurrence
  and forecasting by observation

11. Passage planning   7
- Publications available to assist with planning of
  long passages (routeing charts, ocean passages
  of the world and other publications)

- Preparation for ocean passage including survival
  equipment, victualling, water and fuel management,
  chafe protection, spares and maintenance

12. Passage making   3
- Navigational routine

- Watchkeeping

- Crew management

13. Communications   2
- Satellite and terrestrial systems

- Weather information

RYA Diesel Engine Shorebased Course Syllabus

The course

The aim of the course is to give an awareness of the main systems of a marine diesel engine and the ability to take simple measures to prevent mechanical breakdown at sea and rectify defects which do not require workshop support.

Course duration

The minimum duration of the course is six hours.

A marine diesel engine (not necessarily in working condition) will be provided for practical sessions. (No more than six students to one engine.) Instructors will have attended an RYA training course.

Pre-course knowledge

Nil

1. Introduction

- Principles of the diesel engine

2. The four-stroke cycle

- Naturally aspirated engines • Turbocharging • Intercooling/aftercooling

3. The fuel system

- The basic system • The tank • The water-separating pre-filter
- Fuel lift pump • The engine fine filter • Injection pump
- Injectors • Bleeding the system

4. The cooling system

- Seawater cooling • Freshwater cooling • Temperature control
- The thermostat • The seawater impeller pump

5. The air systems

- The airway in • The airway out

6. Engine electrical systems

- The basic system • Battery capacity and care
- Drive belts • The alternator

7. Spares and tool requirements

- Basic spares and tools

8. Importance of winterisation and servicing

- Engine lubrication • Transmission lubrication
- Winterisation and servicing • Service schedule

9. Fault finding

RYA/MCA Basic Sea Survival for Small Craft

The course
The aim of the course is to give an understanding of how to use the safety equipment carried on small boats, including a practical session in launching and boarding a liferaft.

The instructor will have attended a RYA or other approved training course.

The maximum number of students will be twice the liferaft capacity, (normally 12 to 16).

Course duration
The course duration is one day including a two hour practical session with a liferaft in the water.

Pre-course knowledge
Nil

1. Preparation for sea survival
- Survival difficulties   • Survival requirements
- Equipment available   • Actions prior to abandonment

2. Lifejackets and liferafts
- Lifejacket design and construction - correct donning procedure, purpose and use of lifejackets
- Safety Harness - purpose and use
- Liferafts - towage and containment on board - types, design and construction launching - abandoning the vessel and boarding liferaft - righting a capsized liferaft - liferaft equipment - initial actions to be taken in a liferaft

3. Principles of survival
- Methods to increase chances of survival
- Signs, symptoms and treatment of hypothermia
- Symptoms, method of treatment for sunburn, heat exhaustion and heatstroke
- Survival routines to aid location
- Correct use of pyrotechnics and other location aids
- Water rationing - procedures
- Dehydration and preventative measures
- Food rationing
- Sources of food

4. Survival craft ailments

5. Raft management

6. Search and rescue
- Rescue by helicopter or vessel   • Role of HM Coastguard
- UK and International SAR Organisation   • Other services

RYA Radar Course

The course

The aim of the course is to give an understanding of the use of radar in small boats as an aid to navigation and for collision avoidance.

The course can be conducted ashore using RYA approved software, or afloat on an authorized vessel. The maximum number of students per course will be four afloat or three per screen when conducted ashore. The instructor will have attended an RYA training course.

Course duration

The minimum duration of the course is one day.

Pre-course knowledge

Nil

1. Basic understanding of radar wave propagation
- Conditions giving rise to abnormal propagation

2. Radar set components
- Function and correct use of controls
- Correct setting up procedure

3. Target definition and discrimination
- Spot size, pulse length and beam width
- Target characteristics, size, shape, material
- False echoes
- Shadow sectors, shadow diagram

4. Radar reflectors
- Passive and active

5. Types of radar display
- Azimuth stabilization

6. Radar plotting
- The use of radar to avoid a close quarter situation
- Appreciation of IRPCS, action to be taken in reduced visibility
- General precautions and action to be taken in fog

7. Use of radar as an aid to navigation
- Radar-conspicuous targets, need for positive identification
- Parallel indexing (if provided)

8. Accuracy in range and bearing
- PPI distortion. Non-linearity
- Heading marker alignment
- Checking accuracy of VRM, EBL etc.

9. General safety precautions in using equipment

Course Completion Certificates

The authority to award certificates of satisfactory completion of practical courses is delegated to RYA Training Centres, which may be clubs, sea schools or sea training organisations.

Recognition involves the school being run by a Yachtmaster Instructor, all skippers being qualified, and the vessels used must conform with very stringent regulations laid down by the Maritime and Coastguard Agency and the RYA. Commercial school vessels must carry a Small Commercial Vessel Certificate.

Individual instructors not working as part of a recognised school may not run courses or sign the course sections of the the logbook or issue certificates.

All practical courses are four days minimum cruising on board a motor cruiser (Helmsman two days). On each course the following requirements must be fulfilled:

- The pupil/instructor ratio must not exceed 5:1

- The minimum duration for any course is four days (Helmsman two days). This may be continuous or over weekends

- The instructor will plan an itinerary taking into account the ability of the crew, the weather conditions and the requirements to cover the syllabus

- The motor cruiser should cover a minimum of 100 miles

- Each member of the crew should experience at least four hours of night watch keeping

- The instructor will hold a Yachtmaster Offshore Certificate of Competence (Cruising Instructor)

- For Coastal Skipper courses the instructor will hold a Yachtmaster Offshore Certificate with a current Instructor's endorsement. Instructors are required to update their qualification every five years

- During the Day Skipper and Coastal Skipper courses, each trainee skipper will be given an opportunity to skipper the vessel under instruction and will receive a full debrief during or at the end of the passage

- During each course the instructor will inform the students of their progress and ensure that everyone is aware of their strengths and weaknesses

Own boat tuition

Schools may offer instruction for RYA certificates in a student's boat. Before doing so however, the Principal must ensure that the boat is in sound condition and is adequately equipped both for safety and effective instruction. There is no requirement for a Small Commercial Vessel Certificate for a boat which is being used for the owner's instruction and that of his or her family or friends.

Helmsman's Course

This is a two day boat handling course. It is specific to the type of boat in which the course is carried out and is therefore particularly suitable for new owners of motor cruisers.

Day Skipper

Certificates may be awarded irrespective of whether the candidate holds a certificate of satisfactory completion for the shorebased course. However, the possession of the shorebased course completion certificate will greatly enhance the value of the practical course as the instructor will be able to concentrate on the practical aspects of the syllabus.

Coastal Skipper

This is a course for potential skippers and it is assumed that those attending it will be competent with a good knowledge of the theory of navigation and meteorology, and will already have a level of experience approaching that required for the Coastal Skipper Certificate of Competence.

There is not sufficient time during the course to teach the basic skills of seamanship, helmsmanship and navigation, as well as to teach how these skills should be applied by the skipper of a motor cruiser. Students will be assessed during the course and certificates of satisfactory completion will not be awarded to those who:

- Are adversely affected by sea-sickness to the extent that their ability to skipper a motor cruiser is reduced to a dangerously low level.

- Are unable to demonstrate sufficient ability in basic seamanship, navigation and motor cruiser handling to appreciate the technique and skills required of a motor cruiser skipper.

- Demonstrate a lack of understanding of any part of the syllabus to the extent that it would be dangerous for them to go to sea as the skipper of a motor cruiser.

Non-tidal Courses

These courses are specifically designed for yachtsmen and women who wish to cruise in the Mediterranean and Baltic Seas. Although included in this logbook, the non-tidal skippering courses are quite separate from those gained in tidal waters. There is no conversion course from non-tidal to tidal. If you have taken a non-tidal course and require a tidal certificate it will be necessary to attend another course.

The Helmsman's Course is the same in tidal and non-tidal waters.

Practical training for the Yachtmaster Offshore Certificate

No syllabus is prescribed for a practical course for the Yachtmaster Offshore Certificate. However, training centres may offer courses in preparation for this examination, either to give candidates experience of making longer passages or simply as a refresher course on aspects of motor cruiser handling, navigation and seamanship.

Swimmers

It is strongly recommended that all those participating in the sport of cruising should be able to swim. Non-swimmers will normally be required to wear a lifejacket at all times.

Helmsman's Course Syllabus

Aim: To teach boat handling & safety within a defined area (NDP Code)

A: Theory session

1. Types of craft
- Sportsboat, motor cruisers planing/displacement
- Types of hull, seakeeping, wash considerations

Instructor's signature

2. Engines and drives
- Advantages and disadvantages
- Petrol/diesel
- Single/twin screw
- Shafts/outdrives, outboard, waterjets

Instructor's signature

3. Engine operation and maintenance
- Pre-start checks inboard / outboards
- Engine checks while running
- Routine maintenance checks
- Fuel consumption range, reserve, and location of fuel cut-offs
- Basic fault diagnosis

Instructor's signature

4. Safety and seamanship
- Personal safety equipment – lifejackets, buoyancy aids, flares, first aid kit
- Anchoring: - types, stowage, depth of water, preparation, check holding, weighing. (may be done practically)
- Disabled craft, towing
- Fire precautions, extinguishers, fire blankets

Instructor's signature

5. Rule of the road
- Has a working knowledge of the International Regulations for Preventing Collisions at Sea

Instructor's signature

B: Practical session

1. Boat preparation
- Local boating conditions and regulations
- Preparation of boat, lines, fenders
- Safety equipment, lifejackets, dangers, number in boat
- CE marks, loading, effect on handling and performance
- Use of kill cords
- If trailer - number of people for launching/recovery, slipway condition, steep/slippery, wind, tide
- Can tie & knows use of: bowline, round turn & two half hitches, clove hitch, single & double sheetbend

Instructor's signature

2. Boat handling
- Steering, controls, windage
- Starting and stopping
- Low speed, steering a straight course
- Turning in a confined area
- Effect of wind on bow
- High speed/full power, planning, trim tabs and power trim
- S turns, U turns, stopping from speed
- Displacement craft: handling ahead and astern
- Carrying way

Instructor's signature

3. Securing to a buoy
- Preparation of mooring warp and boathook
- Method of approach in various conditions
- Crew communication
- Making fast

Instructor's signature

4. Alongside

- Preparation and use of lines and springs, fenders, attachment to boat, stowage underway, securing to cleats
- Method of approach in various wind & tide conditions
- Making fast - importance of 'taking a turn'
- Use of springs to leave a berth

Instructor's signature

5. Man overboard

- Immediate reaction
- Proper observation of man overboard
- Correct return
- Awareness of propellers
- Final approach and recovery of man overboard

Instructor's signature

Day Skipper Practical Course Syllabus - Tidal

The Day Skipper course is taught on board a motor cruiser at least 7m LOA and aims to teach pilotage, navigation, seamanship and boat handling up to the standard required to skipper a motor cruiser safely by day in tidal waters with which the student is familiar.

1. Preparation for sea

- Is able to prepare a motor cruiser for sea, carry out fuel and engine checks, securing and stowage of all gear on deck and below

_____
Instructor's signature

2. Boat handling

- Can carry out the following manoeuvres under power in various wind and tide conditions. Has understanding of the different styles of hull and propulsions systems
- Steering a straight course
- Turning in a confined space
- Anchoring at a pre-determined position
- Berthing alongside
- Leaving an alongside berth
- Picking up a mooring buoy
- Correct use of power trim & tabs
- Awareness of other water users

_____
Instructor's signature

3. Navigation

- Is proficient in chart work and can carry out the following tasks:
- Taking and plotting visual fixes
- Use of electronic navigation equipment for position fixing
- Use of waypoints
- Working up DR and EP
- Estimating tidal heights and tidal streams
- Working out course to steer to allow for tidal stream
- Knowledge of IALA buoyage
- Maintenance of navigational records
- Use of echo sounder

_____
Instructor's signature

4. Pilotage

- Can prepare and execute a pilotage plan for entry into, or departure from, harbour

- Understands the use of leading and clearing lines

- Use of transits and soundings as aids to pilotage

Instructor's signature

5. Passage making

- Can plan and make a coastal passage, taking into account the relevant navigational hazards and limitations imposed by the type of boat, weather, tide and the strength of the crew

- Has been introduced to practical benefits and limitations of GPS

Instructor's signature

6. Meteorology

- Knows sources of forecast information, can interpret shipping forecasts and use of a barometer as a forecasting aid

Instructor's signature

7. Rule of the road

- Has a working knowledge of the application of the International Regulations for Preventing Collisions at Sea

Instructor's signature

8 Engines

- Has a working knowledge of the prevention of common engine faults and is competent in the following areas:

- Checks before starting, whilst running and after stopping

- Periodic maintenance checks on engines and electrical installations

- Requirements for tool kits, spares and lubricants

- Can clean water filters & knows location of impellors

- Knows location of filters & bleed points for fuel

- Knows tensions of drive belts & how to change

- Fuel consumption at various speeds & the effect of fouling

Instructor's signature

9. Emergency situations

- Is able to take correct action as skipper for recovery of man overboard

- Can operate a radiotelephone in an emergency and send a distress message

- Understands how to secure a tow, rescue procedures including helicopter rescue

- Understands distress flares and how to use a liferaft

Instructor's signature

10. Night cruising

- Has experienced motor cruising at night, including leaving and entering harbour, and understands the special considerations for pilotage plans, keeping a lookout and identifying marks by night

Instructor's signature

Day Skipper Practical Course Syllabus - Non-Tidal

The Day Skipper course is taught on board a motor cruiser at least 7m LOA and aims to teach pilotage, navigation, seamanship and boat handling up to the standard required to skipper a motor cruiser safely by day in non-tidal waters with which the student is familiar.

1. Preparation for sea

- Is able to prepare a motor cruiser for sea, carry out fuel and engine checks, securing and stowage of all gear on deck and below

Instructor's signature

2. Boat handling

- Can carry out the following manoeuvres under power in various wind and tide conditions

- Has understanding of the different styles of hull and propulsions systems

- Steering a straight course

- Turning in a confined space

- Anchoring at a pre-determined position

- Berthing alongside

- Leaving an alongside berth

- Picking up a mooring buoy

- Correct use of power trim & tabs

- Awareness of other water users

- Berthing bow & stern to

Instructor's signature

3 Navigation

- Is proficient in chart work and can carry out the following tasks:

- Taking and plotting visual fixes

- Use of electronic navigation equipment for position fixing

- Use of waypoints

- Working up DR and EP

- Working out course to steer

- Knowledge of IALA buoyage

- Maintenance of navigational records

- Use of echo sounder

Instructor's signature

4. Passage making

- Can plan and make a coastal passage, taking into account the relevant navigational hazards and limitations imposed by the type of boat, weather, and the strength of the crew

- Has been introduced to practical benefits and limitations of GPS

Instructor's signature

5. Pilotage

- Can prepare and execute a pilotage plan for entry into or departure from harbour

- Understands the use of leading and clearing lines

- Use of transits and soundings as aids to pilotage

Instructor's signature

6. Meteorology

- Knows sources of forecast information, can interpret shipping forecasts and use a barometer as a forecasting aid

Instructor's signature

7. Rule of the road

- Has a working knowledge of the application of the International Regulations for Preventing Collisions at Sea

Instructor's signature

8. Engines

- Has a working knowledge of the prevention of common engine faults and is competent in the following areas:

- Checks before starting, whilst running and after stopping

- Periodic maintenance checks on engines and electrical installations

- Requirements for tool kits, spares and lubricants

- Can clean water filters & knows location of impellors

- Knows location of filters & bleed points for fuel

- Knows tensions of drive belts & how to change

- Fuel consumption at various speeds & the effect of fouling

Instructor's signature

9. Emergency situations

- Is able to take correct action as skipper for recovery of man overboard

- Can operate a radiotelephone in an emergency and send a distress message

- Understands how to secure a tow, rescue procedures including helicopter rescue

- Understands distress flares and how to use a liferaft

_____

Instructor's signature

10.Night cruising

- Has experienced motor cruising at night, including leaving and entering harbour, and understands the special considerations for pilotage plans keeping a lookout and identifying marks by night

_____

Instructor's signature

Coastal Skipper Practical Course Syllabus - Tidal

Aim: To teach the skills and techniques required to skipper a motor cruiser (at least 7m LOA) safely on coastal and offshore passages by day and night.

1 Passage planning

- Can plan a coastal passage including a consideration of the capability of the motor cruiser, navigation, victualling, weather, ports of refuge, tidal heights and tidal steams, publications required and strategy

- Understands fuel consumption at different speeds and can calculate fuel required for passage including reserve

- Aware of effects of fouling on boat speed and fuel consumption

- Knows customs procedures

_____
Instructor's signature

2. Preparation for sea

- Is aware of safety equipment for offshore passages

- Can prepare a motor cruiser for sea including stowage, safety briefing, watch keeping, delegating responsibilities and equipment, fuel and engine checks

_____
Instructor's signature

3. Pilotage

- Can prepare a pilotage plan, with consideration of soundings, transits, clearing bearings, buoyage, port or harbour regulations and tidal considerations

- Can pilot a motor cruiser by day and night

_____
Instructor's signature

4. Passage making and ability as skipper

- Can take charge of the motor cruiser and direct the crew

- Can organise the navigation, deckwork and domestic duties of a motor cruiser on passage

- Is aware of the significance of meteorological trends. Is aware of crew welfare on passage

- Can use electronic navigational equipment for pre-planning and undertaking a passage and can update when underway, especially the use of waypoints and routes

Instructor's signature

5. Radar

- Understands the use of radar as an aid to navigation, pilotage, collision warning and collision avoidance

Instructor's signature

6. Boat handling

- Can control the boat effectively in a confined space including all berthing and unberthing situations in various conditions of wind and tide

- Can berth and unberth in simple situations using one engine on a twin-engined boat. Use of lines during this

- Avoids excessive use of power

Instructor's signature

7. Adverse weather conditions

- Preparation for heavy weather and handling in strong winds

- Navigation and general conduct in restricted visibility

Instructor's signature

8. Emergency situations

- Recovery of man overboard. Understands action to be taken when abandoning to the liferaft and during helicopter and lifeboat rescues

Instructor's signature

Coastal Skipper Practical Course Syllabus - Non Tidal

Aim: To teach the skills and techniques required to skipper a motor cruiser (at least 7m LOA) safely on coastal and offshore passages by day and night in non-tidal waters.

1. Passage planning

- Can plan a coastal passage including a consideration of the capability of the motor cruiser, navigation, victualling, weather, ports of refuge, publications required and strategy

- Understands fuel consumption at different speeds and can calculate fuel required for passage including reserve

- Aware of effects of fouling on boat speed and fuel consumption

- Knows customs procedures

Instructor's signature

2. Preparation for sea

- Is aware of safety equipment for offshore passages

- Can prepare a motor cruiser for sea including stowage, safety briefing, watch keeping, delegating responsibilities and equipment, fuel and engine checks

Instructor's signature

3. Pilotage

- Can prepare a pilotage plan, with consideration of soundings, transits, clearing bearings, buoyage, port or harbour regulations

- Can pilot a motor cruiser by day and night

Instructor's signature

4. Passage making and ability as skipper

- Can take charge of the motor cruiser and direct the crew

- Can organise the navigation, deckwork and domestic duties of a motor cruiser on passage

- Is aware of the significance of meteorological trends

- Is aware of crew welfare on passage

- Can use electronic navigational equipment for pre-planning and undertaking a passage and can update when underway, especially the use of waypoints and routes

5. Radar

- Understands the use of radar as an aid to navigation, pilotage, collision warning and collision avoidance

6. Boat handling

- Can control the boat effectively in a confined space including all berthing and unberthing situations in various wind conditions

- Can berth and unberth in simple situations using one engine on a twin-engined boat. Use of lines during this

- Avoids excessive use of power

7. Adverse weather conditions

- Preparation for heavy weather and handling in strong winds

- Navigation and general conduct in restricted visibility

8. Emergency situations

- Recovery of man overboard

- Understands action to be taken when abandoning to the liferaft and during helicopter and lifeboat rescues

Personal Log

For the Personal Log to be of value it must be filled in accurately and comprehensively. The columns have particular significance in relation to the experience required before examination for certificates of competence. The following notes give guidance on the information to be included and define the terms used.

Personal Log of cruisers and/or races (page 46):

Column 3 Details of voyage
It is most important that this includes a record of your role on the cruise (eg. crew member, mate of watch, skipper etc.)

Column 4 Days on board
A day on board is a period of 24 consecutive hours living on board the vessel. Periods of less than 24 hours may not be aggregated to increase the total but a day is not invalidated by leaving the motor cruiser for a few hours during a cruise.

Column 5 Distance logged
This is the distance covered by the log, in the open sea, outside natural or artificial harbours.

Tidal Certificates
Provided that at least 50% of the qualifying experience for any tidal certificate has been logged in tidal waters, the balance may be made up of experience in non-tidal waters.

Column 6 Night hours
This is hours on watch or taking an active part in the navigation or handling of the motor cruiser at sea between sunset and sunrise.

Column 7 Signature of skipper
Holders of logbooks may sign for cruises during which they were skipper of the motor cruiser.

Retrospective logging of experience
Page 44 includes a section for candidates to record, in general terms, experience gained prior to acquiring the logbook. The experience requirements for examinations for Yachtmaster Offshore and Coastal Skipper should preferably have been gained within 10 years of the examination.

Record of qualifying passages
Full details of the qualifying passages required for the Yachtmaster Offshore examination should be recorded on page 45.

Quality of experience
The requirements for experience prior to examination for RYA/MCA certificates can only be defined in quantitative terms. However, the quality of experience is just as important and although it would be impossible to lay down absolute requirements without producing an unduly complicated and restrictive set of rules, the attention of all candidates is drawn to the following notes.

Geographical breadth of experience

It is relatively simple to visit harbours and anchorages with which one is familiar and has local knowledge. However, a competent skipper should be able to enter any harbour in which there is sufficient depth, given an adequate chart and sailing directions.

The skill of interpreting published information on unfamiliar harbours is best acquired by practice and every opportunity should be taken to visit small harbours and anchorages. Entering harbour by night calls for an acquired skill in identifying navigational lights or picking out unlit marks against the background of the shore lights. Again, practice is the key to success.

Adverse weather conditions

Skippers are most thoroughly tested when they have to cope with gale force winds or fog at sea. It is possible, by cruising within strict self-imposed limits and never going more than a few hours from a safe harbour, to avoid adverse weather conditions. However, to do so invariably limits experience. It is not recommended that anyone should go to sea under adverse conditions for the sole purpose of experiencing a gale or fog but neither should candidates for RYA/MCA certificates adopt an over-cautious approach.

Boat types

Motor Cruiser is a generic term covering a very wide range of boats with different handling characteristics and sea-keeping abilities. It is particularly important to recognise the differences between low-speed displacement boats and high-speed planing ones. Proficiency at handling one does not necessarily imply competence at handling the other and changing between the two types will entail a reappraisal of limiting sea conditions and a relearning of boat handling techniques.

Summary of experience prior to record in personal log

Year	Broad details of experience [1]	Estimated			Skipper's signature [2]
		Days on board	Distance logged	Night hours	

1 include boats sailed, sailing area and capacity in which sailed
2 if available

RYA/MCA offshore qualifying passages

Port of departure time date	Destination time date	Distance	Sailing capacity	Skipper's signature
Harwich *1830 23.8.98*	*Ostende* *1510 24.8.98*	*79M*	*Crew*	*J Mendez*

Specimen entry

RYA/MCA Yachtmaster Ocean passage

Passage completed on board yacht ....

Type of yacht, inc LOA ....

Port of departure ....Time/Date ....

Port of arrival ....Time/Date ....

Over 50M from land between position ....Time/Date ....

and position ....Time/Date ....

a total of .... hours, for a distance of .... miles

Sailing as Skipper/Mate of Watch (delete as appropriate) throughout the passage.

Total distance sailed .... M

Signature of Skipper ....

Personal log of cruises and/or races

1. Dates From To	2. Name of vessel Class, size inc LOA or tonnage	3. Details of voyage max wind force, ports visited, capacity in which sailing	4. Days on board	5. Distance logged tidal/non-tidal	6. Night hours	7. Skipper's signature
Specimen entry 20-25th Aug 2002	ALPHA Sealine 742	Lymington-Cherbourg-Alderney-St. Peter Port-Lymington. Mate of watch. Max. wind Force 6 on return passage. otherwise F3-4	5	195 Tidal	9	J Mendez

Totals carried forward

Personal log of cruises and/or races

Totals carried forward

1. Dates From To	2. Name of vessel Class, size inc LOA or tonnage	3. Details of voyage max wind force, ports visited, capacity in which sailing	4. Days on board	5. Distance logged tidal/non-tidal	6. Night hours	7. Skipper's signature

47

Personal log of cruises and/or races

Totals brought forward

Totals carried forward

1. Dates From To	2. Name of vessel Class, size inc LOA or tonnage	3. Details of voyage max wind force, ports visited, capacity in which sailing	4. Days on board	5. Distance logged tidal/non-tidal	6. Night hours	7. Skipper's signature

Personal log of cruises and/or races

Totals carried forward

1. Dates From To	2. Name of vessel Class, size inc LOA or tonnage	3. Details of voyage max wind force, ports visited, capacity in which sailing	4. Days on board	5. Distance logged tidal/non-tidal	6. Night hours	7. Skipper's signature

49

Summary of personal log

	Day	Distance logged	Night hours
TOTALS FOR 20..			
TOTALS FOR 20..			
TOTALS FOR 20..			
TOTALS FOR 20..			
TOTALS FOR 20..			
TOTALS FOR 20..			
TOTALS FOR 20..			
TOTALS FOR 20..			
TOTALS FOR 20..			
TOTALS FOR 20..			
TOTALS			

PRACTICAL COURSE
RYA HELMSMAN

ATTACH YOUR CERTIFICATE HERE

SHOREBASED COURSE
RYA DAY SKIPPER

ATTACH YOUR CERTIFICATE HERE

PRACTICAL COURSE
RYA DAY SKIPPER NON -TIDAL

ATTACH YOUR CERTIFICATE HERE

PRACTICAL COURSE
RYA DAY SKIPPER TIDAL

ATTACH YOUR CERTIFICATE HERE

SHOREBASED COURSE
RYA/MCA COASTAL SKIPPER AND YACHTMASTER OFFSHORE

ATTACH YOUR CERTIFICATE HERE

PRACTICAL COURSE
RYA/MCA COASTAL SKIPPER NON-TIDAL

ATTACH YOUR CERTIFICATE HERE

PRACTICAL COURSE
RYA/MCA COASTAL SKIPPER TIDAL

ATTACH YOUR CERTIFICATE HERE

SHOREBASED COURSE
RYA/MCA YACHTMASTER OCEAN

ATTACH YOUR CERTIFICATE HERE

SHOREBASED COURSE
DIESEL ENGINE COURSE

ATTACH YOUR CERTIFICATE HERE

PRACTICAL COURSE
RYA/MCA BASIC SEA SURVIVAL FOR SMALL CRAFT

ATTACH YOUR CERTIFICATE HERE

SHOREBASED COURSE
RYA RADAR COURSE

ATTACH YOUR CERTIFICATE HERE

Examination centres

Southern
Royal Yachting Association
RYA House
Ensign Way
Hamble Southampton
Hampshire SO31 4YA
Tel: 0845 345 0400

East Anglia
West Mersea Yacht Club
116 Coast Road
West Mersea
Colchester   CO5 8PB
Tel: 01206 383306

Wales
RYA Examination Centre
16 Friars Road
Barry Island
Glamorgan CF62 8TR
Tel: 01446 734836

Scotland
RYA Scotland
Caledonia House
South Gyle
Edinburgh
EH12 9DQ
Tel: 0131 317 7388

Examinations for service personnel are also conducted by the JSASTC, RNSA, RAFSA, and ASA. Servicemen should consult the JSASTC or their Sailing Association for details of examination arrangements.

NAME ....

ADDRESS ....

....

....

CHANGE OF ADDRESS ....

....

....

Notes

Notes

Notes

Notes

RYA *Membership*

Promoting and Protecting Boating
www.rya.org.uk

The RYA is the national organisation which represents the interests of everyone who goes boating for pleasure.

The greater the membership, the louder our voice when it comes to protecting members' interests.

Apply for membership today, and support the RYA, to help the RYA support you.

Benefits of Membership

- Access to expert advice on all aspects of boating from legal wrangles to training matters

- Special members' discounts on a range of products and services including boat insurance, books, videos and class certificates

- Free issue of certificates of competence, increasingly asked for by everyone from overseas governments to holiday companies, insurance underwriters to boat hirers

- Access to the wide range of RYA publications, including the quarterly magazine

- Third Party insurance for windsurfing members

- Free Internet access with RYA-Online

- A privilege price structure for purchasing a Volvo car

- Regular offers in RYA Magazine

- ...and much more

Join online at ***www.rya.org.uk***
or use the form overleaf.

Visit the website for information, advice, member services and web shop.

If you have previously been a member and know your membership number please enter here

When completed, please send this form to: RYA RYA House Ensign Way Hamble Southampton SO31 4YA

	Tick box	Cash/Chq.	DD
Family		£44	£41
Personal		£28	£25
Under 21		£11	£11

Please indicate your main area of interest

❏ Yacht Racing ❏ Dinghy Cruising ❏ Powerboat Racing
❏ Yacht Cruising ❏ Personal Watercraft ❏ Windsurfing
❏ Dinghy Racing ❏ Inland Waterways ❏ Motor Boating
❏ Sportsboats and RIBs

† Family Membership = 2 adults plus any U21's all living at the same address.

For details of Life Membership and paying over the phone by Credit/Debit card, please call 0845 345 0374/5 or join online at www.rya.org.uk

PLEASE USE BLOCK CAPITALS

Title Forename Surname Date of Birth Male Female

1.
2.
3.
4.

Address

Town County Postcode

Home Phone No. Day Phone No.

Facsimile No. Mobile No.

Email Address

Signature _____ Date _____

RYA

Instructions to your Bank or Building Society to pay by Direct Debit

DIRECT Debit

Please fill in the form and send to:
RYA RYA House Ensign Way Hamble Southampton SO31 4YA   Tel: 0845 345 0400

Name and full postal address of your Bank/Building Society

To The Manager   Bank/Building Society
Address

Postcode

Name(s) of Account Holder(s)

Bank/Building Society account number

Branch Sort Code

Originator's Identification Number

9	5	5	2	1	3

Reference Number

Instruction to your Bank or Building Society
Please pay Royal Yachting Association Direct Debits from the account detailed in this instruction subject to the safeguards assured by The Direct Debit Guarantee. I understand that this instruction may remain with the Royal Yachting Association and, if so, details will be passed electronically to my Bank/Building Society.

Signature(s)

Date

Banks and Building Societies may not accept Direct Debit Instructions for some types of account

---

OR YOU CAN PAY BY CHEQUE

Source Code
077

Cheque enclosed £ Made payable to the Royal Yachting Association

Office use only: Membership number allocated